ALL THAT JA

FOR
ALTO SAXOPHONE
ALTO SAXOPHONE
ALT SAXAPHON

WITH PIANO ACCOMPANIMENT
MIT KLAVIERBEGLEITUNG
ACCOMPAGNEMENT AU PIANO

Editor: James Power

Contents

CHESTER MUSIC
Order No. PM1943101R

EDITOR'S NOTE

Welcome to "All That Jazz".

Many Saxophone players would like to try a little jazz. This book contains a collection of melodic, playable jazz and modern themes for Saxophone with piano/keyboard accompaniment.

Most pieces contain a theme and an "ad lib" chorus. A suggested "ad lib" is written but the students may like to improvise their own.

After practising the Saxophone part, get together with a piano student – the result could surprise you.

To play a bit of jazz can be a most enjoyable and rewarding experience. Try it.

VORBEMERKUNG DES HERAUSGEBERS

Herzlich willkommen an 'All That Jazz'.

Viele Saxophonstudenten wurden gern ein bißchen Jazz probieren. Dieses Buch enthält eine Sammlung von melodischen und Spielbaren Jazz, und auch modernen Melodien für die Saxophonstudenten mit Klavier/Keyboardbegleitung.

Die meisten Stücke haben ein Thema und einen improvisierten Refrain. Obgleigh ein vorgeschlagener Refrain hier geschrieben wird, dürfen die Studenten improvisieren wie sie wollen.

Nachdem Sie die Saxophonstudenten Melodie gut geübt haben, versuchen Sie die Melodie zusammen mit einem Klavier zu spielen. Ihnen könnte das Resultat günstig überraschen.

Eine Kassette ist vorhanden.

Viel Spaß und eine lohnende Erfahrung kommen schnell wenn ein bißchen Jazz gut gespielt wird. Probieren Sie es!

Bienvenue à 'All That Jazz'

Beaucoup de saxophonistes aimeraient jouer un peu de jazz. Ce livre contient une collection de mélodies de jazz qui sont jouables, ainsi que des thèmes modernes pour saxophone avec accompagnement piano/clavier.

Bon nombre de pièces contiennent un thème et un chorus 'ad libitum'. Il est suggéré l'un de ces chorus, mais les étudiants pourraient préférer improviser.

Après avoir étudié la partie saxophone, demandez à un pianiste de se joindre à vous: vous serez surpris du résultat!

Jouer un peu de jazz peut être une expérience fort agréable et très satisfaisante. Essayez!

When the Saints go Marching In

Arr. Power

Golden Mile

James Power

Rag Doll

James Power

Solitude

James Power

Sugar Fly

James Blackford
Arr. Power

17

Brown and Blue

James Power

Jam Session

James Blackford
Arr. Power

Down the Road

James Power

29

Skive Jive

James Power

Sidewalks of Harlem

James Power

Bill Bailey

Arr. Power

38

Tannakins Dance

Based on a theme by
Gabriel-Marie 1852-1928
Arr. Power

BLUE
SAXOPHONE
James Rae

UNIVERSAL EDITION

TENOR
SAXOPHONE

Mr Creek

JAMES RAE

Vintage Blue

JAMES RAE

UE 19765bL

Waltz for Emily

JAMES RAE

In the Wee Small Hours

JAMES RAE

Rachel and the Boys

JAMES RAE

UE 19765bL

UE 19765bL

Reproduced and printed by
Halstan & Co. Ltd., Amersham, Bucks., England

18826	P. HARVEY/J. SANDS	JAZZY CLARINET 1
19361	P. HARVEY	JAZZY CLARINET 2
18827	J. RAE	JAZZY SAXOPHONE 1
19362	J. RAE	JAZZY SAXOPHONE 2
19393	J. RAE	JAZZY TRUMPET 1
18825	J. REEMAN	JAZZY FLUTE 1
19360	J. REEMAN	JAZZY FLUTE 2
18824	J. REEMAN	JAZZY PIANO 1
19363	B. BONSOR/G. RUSSELL-SMITH	JAZZY PIANO 2
18828	G. RUSSELL-SMITH	JAZZY RECORDER 1
19364	B. BONSOR	JAZZY RECORDER 2
19431	M. RADANOVICS	JAZZY VIOLIN 1
19757	M. RADANOVICS	JAZZY VIOLIN 2
16553	M. RADANOVICS	JAZZY CELLO 1
19711	T. DRUMMOND	JAZZY GUITAR 1
19429	J. RAE	JAZZY DUETS FOR FLUTES
19430	J. RAE	JAZZY DUETS FOR CLARINETS
19395	J. RAE	JAZZY DUETS FOR SAXOPHONE
19396	J. RAE	JAZZY DUETS FOR FLUTE and CLARINET
19756	M. CORNICK	JAZZY DUETS FOR PIANO
16536	M. CORNICK	JAZZY DUETS FOR PIANO 2
16537	M. RADANOVICS	JAZZY DUETS FOR VIOLIN

CHRISTMAS JAZZ

19184	J. RAE	CHRISTMASJAZZ FOR FLUTE
19186	J. RAE	CHRISTMASJAZZ FOR TRUMPET
19187	J. RAE	CHRISTMASJAZZ FOR CLARINET
19188	J. RAE	CHRISTMASJAZZ FOR ALTO SAXOPHONE
19189	J. RAE	CHRISTMASJAZZ FOR CELLO
19190	J. RAE	CHRISTMASJAZZ FOR TROMBONE
19185	J. RAE	CHRISTMASJAZZ FOR VIOLIN

VI/94

UNIVERSAL EDITION